"Nursing is an art;
and if it is to be made an art,
it requires as exclusive a devotion,
as hard a preparation,
as any painter's or sculptor's work;

...It is one of the Fine Arts;
I had almost said
the finest of the Fine Arts."

Florence Nightingale
1820-1910

In memory of my great grandmother, Jane,
who never recovered from her loss.

HR

For my nan, '*Little Lily*'
and for her daughter, my darling mum.

MI

first printed March 2018

STRAUSS HOUSE PRODUCTIONS
www.strausshouseproductions.com

First published in Great Britain 2018
Text copyright © Hilary Robinson 2018
Illustrations copyright © Martin Impey 2018
Hilary Robinson and Martin Impey have asserted their rights
to be identified as the author and illustrator of this work under
The Copyright, Designs and Patents Act, 1988
British Library Cataloguing in Publication Data
A catalogue record for this book is available from the British Library
All rights reserved. ISBN - 978-0-9571245-5-4
Printed in the UK

PEACE LILY

by
Hilary Robinson & Martin Impey

STRAUSS HOUSE
PRODUCTIONS

The November frost was biting
The day Lily was born.

The world was calm, all was still,
That icy, misty morn.

Taking her name from a flower
Her father had seen by the lane,
"You'll light up the dark," he said to her,
"And bring hope to a world in pain."

Lily played with friends Ray and Ben,
They picnicked on apples and cheese,

They paddled in brooks and ran in the woods
And hid in the old willow trees.

"It's Lily, it's me!" Lily would sing
When she found the boys in the dell.

They'd listen to larks and gather wild fruit
And play by the old water well.

But dark clouds of war were looming,
And the boys became men and joined ranks,

Their childhood was gone, new days now dawned
Of battlefields, weapons and tanks.

Lily watched as her friends marched on foot
To fight in lands far away.
And weekly she sent them a letter of hope,
"It's Lily, it's me!" she would say.

Sad that her friends had departed,
And seeing signs that said: *YOU!*
Make Nursing Your War Job! Help The Troops!

Lily joined the war effort too.

Lily arrived at the battlefield
To nurse in a hospital tent,

A place for emergency medical need
Where all the wounded were sent.

Then, one night, when all appeared calm,
Commotion broke out in the bay.

A soldier arrived, so badly hurt,
The padre was called in to pray.

Lily looked, then looked again
At the soldier brought in by the men –

Injured and in a deep sleep, Lily cried,
"It's Ben, my village friend, Ben!"

Night after night, she said to herself,
"I'll make you better, you'll see."

And then, at dawn, as skylarks awoke,
She sang, "Ben, it's Lily, it's me."

Back home with care Ben recovered,
And in time his friends returned too,

While guns and weapons fell silent in
The fields where poppies then grew.

On the eleventh hour of the eleventh day of the eleventh month in 1918,
the guns across Europe fell silent.

The November frost was sparkling
The day a new world was born.

For Ray and Ben and Lily at last there was
Peace... that beautiful morn.

Our Wedding 1920

Our Charlie 1925

Our little Molly Rose. 1928

1932 Southwold

Ray   Lily   Ben

And Buster!!

Happy Memories
1909

Passchendaele
1917

Dads Army!

Our Anniversary

"My Life"

1940 A visit from our
old friends

Thank you
Jackie Hamley, Jim Millea, Megan Brownrigg, Gary Brandham, Joke de Winter,
Nerys Spofforth, Nicky Stonehill, Jessica Ward, Dan Purvis, Helen Nicholson,
Paul Reed (ww1revisited.com), Leighton Buzzard Narrow Gauge Railway (www.buzzrail.co.uk),
Matthew Ward, Pauline McMahon,
and always a very special *'Thank you'* to Andrew Robinson and Emilie James.

Also by
Hilary Robinson & Martin Impey

ISBN - 978-0-9571245-8-5

ISBN - 978-0-9571245-7-8

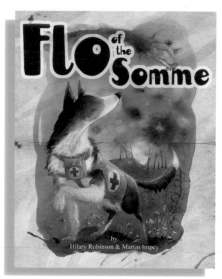

ISBN - 978-0-9571245-6-1

ISBN - 978-0-9571245-3-0

Dulce et Decorum est
by Wilfred Owen

Martin Impey's artistic
interpretation of one of
the greatest war poems
ever written.

Readers 13 +

ISBN - 978-1-5272182-5-3

These award-winning titles have gained recognition in countless schools,
libraries and museums as well as featuring proudly on home bookshelves throughout the UK and beyond.

"Children will never look at poppies in the same way again." Paul Reed – Military Historian

For more information about Strauss House Productions
www.strausshouseproductions.com

'Like us' on Facebook - Where The Poppies Now Grow